Jim the spaceman is going into space in a rocket.

His friends wave goodbye.

Count the rockets.

How many of Jim's friends can you see?

Jim's rocket zooms past some big, yellow moons and some beautiful shooting stars.

Count the moons.

How many shooting stars can you see?

Jim lands his rocket
on Planet Rock.

Some little green men
come to meet him.

Count the little green men.

Hello Jim

Planet
Rock

The little green men
throw a party for Jim.

There are blue and
purple desserts to eat.

How many desserts are
there altogether?

The little green men take
Jim on a tour of Planet Rock.

They show Jim their little
planet pets.

How many planet pets
can you see?